My Unicorn Garden

Activity Book

Published in the UK by Scholastic Children's Books, 2021
Euston House, 24 Eversholt Street, London, NW1 1DB
A division of Scholastic Limited

London ~ New York ~ Toronto ~ Sydney ~ Auckland
Mexico City ~ New Delhi ~ Hong Kong

Text written by Emily Hibbs
Illustrations by Natalie Briscoe
Helen Bostock — RHS Senior Horticultural Advisor
Andrew Salisbury — RHS Principal Scientist Entomology

ISBN 978 0702 30245 9

Printed and bound in the UK by Bell & Bain Ltd, Glasgow
Papers used by Scholastic Children's Books are made from wood grown
in sustainable forests.

2 4 6 8 10 9 7 5 3 1

www.scholastic.co.uk

My Unicorn Garden

Activity Book

SCHOLASTIC

Welcome to the Unicorn Garden

Enter an enchanted garden where unicorns run wild and free! The unicorns will visit four seasonal gardens to discover spring flower beds, summer vegetable patches, autumn treetops and a wintery frozen lake.

This beautiful book is packed with fun facts and amazing activities, so you can discover the wonderful secrets of gardening, with some magical, mythical unicorn friends.

Turn the page to begin!

Once you have completed the activities, check your answers on page 96.

Contents

Outdoor Safety
for Parents and Children

BEFORE THE ADVENTURE BEGINS...

Inspiring children to enjoy plants and gardening can give them a healthy hobby for their whole lives. Gardens are great to have and wonderful to be in, but they do have their hazards, particularly for children. We hope you and your child have lots of fun exploring the activities in this book, so we've come up with some top tips to help you complete all the activities safely.

We want our young gardeners to have a great time discovering new things, so it's important that they learn about boundaries and how to keep safe. Read these pages carefully together with your child to help them stay safe and enjoy the fun of gardening.

We trust that you will make your own judgement about what is safe and suitable for the age and ability of your child. We also recommend that an adult supervises all of our activities.

GET READY TO GARDEN

Never, for any reason, leave children unattended outdoors or in the garden, especially near water. Although it's not considered a substitute for adult supervision, fences are a good way to keep children from wandering into dangerous areas. Consider fencing in ponds, or place a protective mesh cover or metal grid over your pond. Also, empty water out of full hoses, buckets and watering cans, and be careful not to leave water accessible to young children.

Make sure your child knows good plants from bad ones. Teach them never to eat any plants from the garden without the explicit consent of an adult. Point out any unsafe plants that may sting or prick them in the garden and elsewhere, such as rose bushes, holly and cactus plants. In fact, it may be a good idea to avoid these plants altogether if you have young children.

Be aware of any specific plant and food allergies or hay fever. It is advisable to wear gloves when gardening, especially if plants are a skin irritant.

Teach children to respect animal life and not to harm living creatures. Some insects have stings including honeybees and social wasps and a few caterpillars have hairs that can induce rashes. Children should be made aware of the habitats and favourite hangouts of some of these insects as well. Explain to children not to touch or swat at these creatures.

Don't leave garden tools unattended. While it's okay to provide children with tools of their own, be sure they are specifically designed for children and are only used with adult supervision. Teach children the proper way to use them and when, and how to put them safely away after each use. Always help children if sharp tools are to be used.

Finally, always encourage children to wash their hands after being outdoors and in the garden.

OUTSIDE EXPLORERS

Explain to your child that before they go hunting for flowers or exploring in the garden, it's always best to make sure that they check with their parent or guardian first. Children should take care when they are outside, always wearing shoes and keeping an eye out for sharp objects. Before your child takes on one of the active challenges, help them to pick a spot that is safe and suitable for their ability level.

Children can play outside in the cold weather provided they are suitably dressed – lots of warm layers and waterproofs! The sun is more dangerous than we think – remember to encourage children to wear sunhats, sunblock and drink plenty of water. Stay in the shadier parts of the garden.

NATURE TASTERS

Food tastes best when it's freshly picked, but you should avoid putting anything in your mouth when you're outdoors unless you know it's safe to eat. This is especially true of mushrooms and berries, which can be poisonous when eaten. If you're enjoying a picnic outdoors, you should avoid any areas where livestock has been and always wash your hands thoroughly before eating.

Magical Map

Inside the magical garden, all four seasons come alive. The unicorns will discover spring flowerbeds, summer vegetable patches, autumn treetops and a wintery frozen lake.

Start the adventure by colouring in the scene and doodling some more details.

Draw some hatchlings in the nest.

Spring Garden

Add a few more pretty flowers.

Summer Garden

Sketch lots of little snowflakes falling from the sky.

Winter Garden

Draw a unicorn ice skating.

Autumn Garden

Make the pile of fallen leaves even bigger.

Time to Explore

The unicorns can't wait to gallop off on their garden adventure and they'd love for you to join them! Which path will lead the unicorns to the enchanted garden?

Enchanted Garden

Start

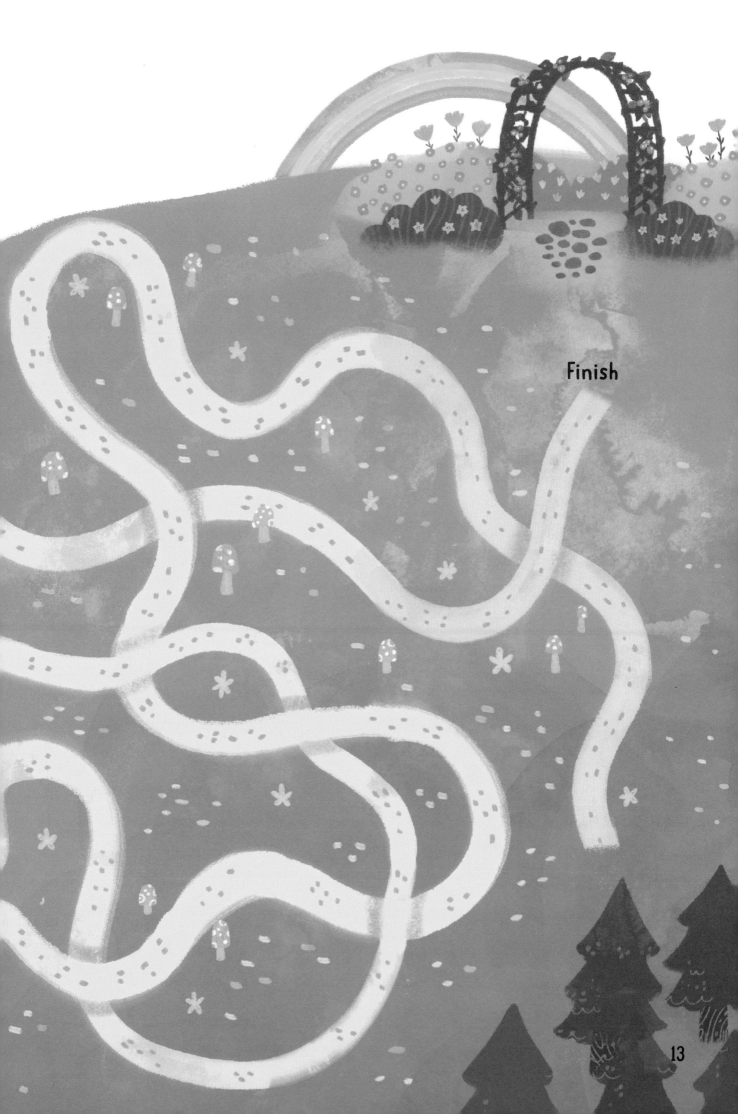

Finish

13

My Magical Unicorn

You and your friends each have a secret unicorn identity that's just waiting to be discovered...

Follow the steps below to reveal the unique unicorn in you. For example, if you were born in May and your favourite flower is a tulip, your name would be Rainbow Stardust.

Pick the month you were born in:

January: Newmoon

February: Shimmermist

March: Rainbowshine

April: Twinkleshy

May: Rainbow

June: Ivyqueen

July: Fireglow

August: Goldenhorn

September: Nightglimmer

October: Flowerbloom

November: Moonbeam

December: Shadowplay

Pick your favourite flower:

Rose: Sunshine

Daisy: Starlight

Lily: Princess

Tulip: Stardust

Sunflower: Sparkle

Daffodil: Twinkle

MY UNICORN NAME IS:

· ·

MY FRIEND'S UNICORN NAME IS:

· ·

Follow the steps to create your own magical unicorn.

Use the space on this page to draw your unicorn, or use another piece of paper to practise first.

Spring Garden

The unicorns have arrived in the Spring Garden. New shoots are sprouting, flowers are blossoming and birds are singing in the trees.

Can you spot all of the beautiful spring blooms in the flowerbed?

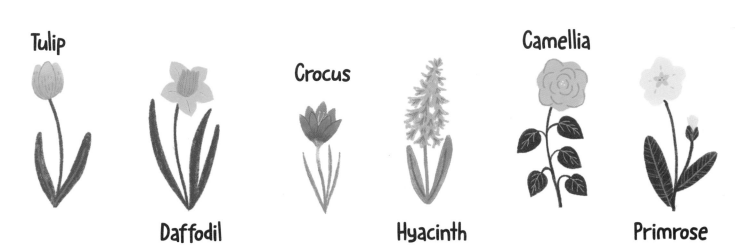

Tulip

Daffodil

Crocus

Camellia

Hyacinth

Primrose

A Rainbow of Flowers

Flowers come in so many shapes and sizes — and so many colours!
Learn about a fabulous flower for every colour of the rainbow.

Rose
These flowers grow in lots of
different colours, but red roses
are the world's favourite.

Marigold
With their bright orange
blooms, these plants
brighten any flowerbed.

Hibiscus
Growing in tropical
climates, these flowers
and can be pink, purple,
white or sunny
yellow.

Clematis
Clematis are climbing plants which like to grow with their heads (flowers) in the sun but their feet (roots) in the shade.

Blue Wild indigo
The leaves of this beautiful flower were used to make a dye in the past.

Cornflower
Bees and butterflies are attracted to these bright blue flowers.

Bells of Ireland
These are one of the few plants that grow green flowers.

Blooming Bulbs

Fill your garden with colourful flowers
by planting some spring bulbs.

You will need:

- a selection of spring bulbs, such as daffodils, tulips, grape hyacinths or crocuses
- patch of soil (or a plant pot filled with soil if you don't have much outside space)
- garden compost
- trowel
- recycled ice-lolly sticks
- paints
- felt-tip pen
- watering can

Step one: use your trowel to remove any rocks or weeds from your patch of soil.

Step two: sprinkle some garden compost over the patch and then turn the soil with your trowel, so that it's mixed together.

Plant your bulbs from late August to October.

Step three: plant your bulbs according to the instructions on the packet — make sure the tips are pointing up. Different bulbs should be planted at different depths in the ground, as per the instructions.

Step four: paint your ice-lolly sticks with bright colours. Once they are dry, write the names of your flowers in clear letters. Stick your colourful plant markers in the ground to help you remember which bulb is which.

Step five: sprinkle some water over your bulbs so the soil is damp. Throughout the autumn and winter, they shouldn't need much watering, but if the weather is especially dry then use your watering can to give them a drink.

Step six: in the spring, your beautiful bulbs will flower, filling the garden with colour.

Always ask an adult for help when gardening. Remember, you'll also need their permission first.

Delightful Daisies

Add splashes of colour to this spectacular, sunny scene.

D.I.Y. Daisy Chains

The unicorns are making daisy chains to wear in their flowing manes.
Learn how to make one for you and your friends.

You will need:

- Daisies, or other stemmed flowers

Always ask an adult before picking flowers.

Step one: using your fingernail, cut a slit in the stem of a daisy, 5 cm below the flower blossom.

Step two: carefully thread another daisy stem into the slit and pull it all the way through up to the flower head.

Step three: repeat the first step by cutting a slit into the stem of the second daisy and then thread another new flower through it.

Step four: repeat these steps until you reach the desired length of your daisy chain.

Flower Pressing

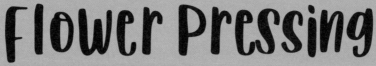

Pressed flowers can be used in all kinds of creative projects, from collages to greetings cards.

You will need:

- a selection of flowers (make sure you have permission to pick them and try not to pull up the roots of the plant)
- a selection of heavy books (the thicker the better)
- white tissue paper

You'll need to ask for permission before you pick any flowers.

Step one: open one book down the middle and line the pages with tissue paper.

Step two: place the flowers you want to press onto one of the pages, carefully smoothing out the petals and leaves so they lie flat.

Step three: gently close the book, then stack a few more heavy books on top to help press the flowers.

Step four: leave the pile of books in a warm, dry place. Check on your flowers every couple of days until the petals are stiff and crackle when touched. Now you can get crafty with your pretty pressed flowers.

Brilliant Butterflies

Bright butterflies are darting all around the Spring Garden
and the unicorns love watching them flutter.

Draw lines to match up the pairs of identical butterflies.

Draw the other half of this beautiful butterfly, then add some bright colours.

Down by the Pond

The unicorns have trotted over to the garden pond and are watching the sunlight sparkling off the water. Below the surface, the watery world is even more magical...

There are ten tadpoles swimming in the pond.
Can you spot them all?

Pond Puzzles

What comes next in these pond patterns? Draw a picture to complete each sequence.

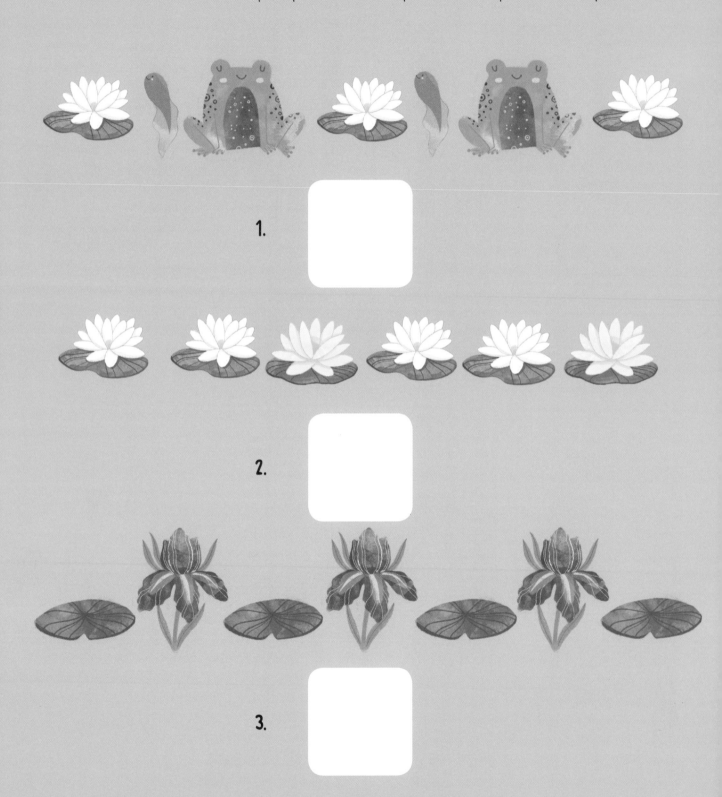

1.

2.

3.

The unicorns have spotted some pretty floating flowers.
Trace over the lines to draw a water lily,
and then colour it in.

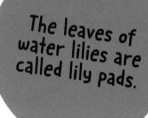

The leaves of water lilies are called lily pads.

Flower Trail

Can you help the unicorns find their way through the Summer Garden?
Use the key below to help you find the path through the grid.

Key:  = up   = down   = left   = right

Start

Finish

Lots of baby animals are born in springtime.
Sketch some of your favourite cute creatures,
and then name each of them.

Summer Garden

The unicorns have galloped into the Summer Garden. The bright sunshine beams down and the flowerbeds are full of colour.

Find the names of these summer flowers hidden in the grid on page 35. Be sure to look forwards, backwards and diagonally.

Lily

Lavender

Daisy

Jasmine

Rose

Sunflower

Summer Garden

L	C	P	X	Q	J	W	M	O	M	T	E	L	S
J	I	D	R	Q	L	E	A	H	F	O	N	H	L
T	S	L	D	J	C	P	A	N	O	L	Y	I	A
E	C	K	Y	C	A	J	I	H	F	A	X	B	V
N	O	M	L	D	H	S	Q	D	G	V	M	G	L
N	I	W	A	N	O	P	M	R	P	E	V	S	S
H	F	G	U	G	A	F	E	I	Z	N	T	U	S
E	A	F	R	O	S	E	G	B	N	D	K	A	U
C	B	R	A	T	I	K	N	E	G	E	J	Y	T
D	Y	T	D	C	W	X	S	S	R	R	Z	A	B
K	A	A	B	A	W	J	H	K	L	M	J	B	E
A	L	I	H	I	S	U	N	F	L	O	W	E	R
P	G	T	S	V	P	E	Y	V	P	A	L	C	I
A	Q	T	P	Y	U	V	A	P	W	I	C	Z	N

Draw some more flowers blooming from each stem.

BUSY BEES

The garden is full of honeybees, buzzing around collecting pollen and nectar from the flowers. Guide this bee back to her hive, stopping at all five flowers along the way.

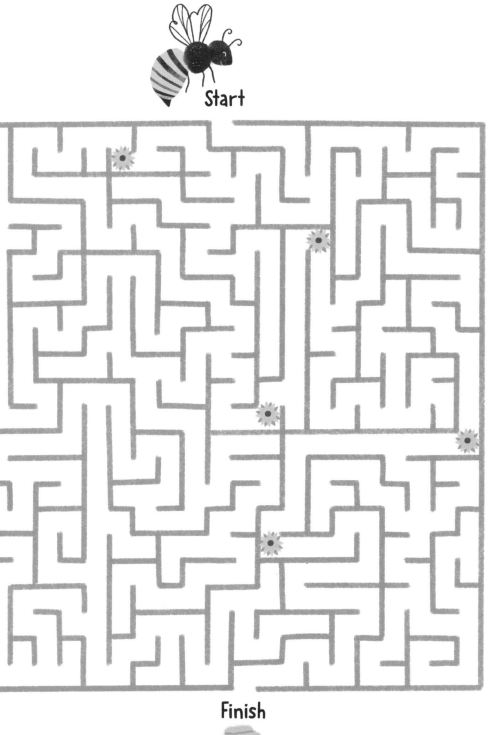

Start

Finish

In this flower patch, the best pollen and juiciest nectar can be found on a purple flower with five petals and a pink centre. Can you spot it?

Pretty Pots

Add some plants to these magical pots, and then colour them in. Flick through this book for inspiration, or make up your own fantastic flowers.

Paint a Unicorn Pot

Create a sweet, sparkly unicorn pot. It's perfect for displaying a pretty plant or to give as a gift.

You will need:

- terracotta plant pot
- white paint
- paint brush
- black permanent marker pen
- glittery card
- white card
- coloured card
- safety scissors
- liquid glue

Ask an adult to help you with the scissors and paints in this fun activity.

Step one: paint your pot white. Keep adding layers until it's completely covered, leaving each layer to dry before starting the next one.

Step two: once the paint is completely dry, draw your unicorn's eyes with the black permanent marker. They could be closed or open, or perhaps even winking!

Step three: cut a horn shape out of the glittery card, two ears out of the white card and some flower shapes out of the coloured card.

Step four: glue the horn and ears inside your pot. Stick the flowers on the outside, so that your unicorn has a pretty flower crown.

Step five: pop your favourite plant in your unicorn pot, or give it to a friend who loves gardening.

Flower Power

Use your colouring pencils to reveal the special flowers, following the key below.

1. blue   2. yellow   3. green   4. brown

Tasty Treats

From juicy fruits to crunchy vegetables, lots of the unicorns' favourite foods can be found growing in the garden. Can you match the pieces below with the spaces in the picture?

A.

B.

C.

D.

E.

Picking strawberries is lots of fun, but it looks like some slugs have got to them first.
How many slugs can you count?

Grow your Own salad

Do you love a healthy lunch as much as the unicorns?
Discover how to grow your own delicious salad from seeds.

You will need:

- an area of the garden
- trowel
- spade
- garden compost

- a selection of seeds, such as lettuce, rocket, spring onion and cucumber
- watering can

Ask an adult to help you with this simple gardening activity.

Step one: clear an area of the garden, removing all weeds and big rocks with your trowel.

Step two: sprinkle over some garden compost. Dig your trowel or a spade into the ground and turn over the soil, so that the compost is thoroughly mixed in. Smooth over the area with the back of your spade.

Step three: plant your seeds according to the instructions on the packets. You could plant them in rows, spirals or patterns – just make sure there's enough space between them for watering and weeding.

Step four: in dry weather, make sure you water your salad garden every day. The ground should always be a little damp, but don't let it get too soggy. Keep an eye out for weeds or slugs and, being careful not to damage your crops, remove any that you spot.

Step five: when your salad crops are ready, create a crunchy side dish to share with friends and family. Make sure you give everything a good wash before serving up.

Picnic Party

The unicorns are having a picnic in the garden with lots of delicious food.
Write down or draw some of your favourite picnic snacks on their plates.

Fantastic Fruit

The unicorns are exploring the magical grove where fruit trees from around the world grow. Learn more about all the fabulous fruit, and then colour in the picture once you've found them all.

Apple trees are best planted with a partner apple tree so they can swap pollen and set good fruit.

This sharp citrus fruit grows all year round. Lemon trees love warm climates. They grow in North and South America, Europe and Asia.

A fruit is the part of a flowering plant that contains seeds. Apples, lemons, oranges and coconuts are fruits.

When oranges were first cultivated in southeast Asia, they were green, not orange! Today, they are grown in lots of tropical and subtropical countries.

As well as the fleshy part of the coconut, the milk, water and oil can also be used in cooking. Coconuts grow on coconut palm trees and are mostly found in tropical areas of South America, Africa and Asia.

Fruit Fun

An apple a day makes a unicorn neigh! How many green apples and red apples can you count in this enchanting orchard?

Green apples: Red apples:

The unicorns' favourite dessert is a delicious fresh fruit salad. Use the key below to help you crack the code and work out which ingredient is missing from the mix.

= A

= P

= E

= L

= N

= I

Write the answer below:

___ ___ ___ ___ ___ ___ ___ ___ ___

Beautiful Birds

The unicorns are admiring some feathered friends they've spotted in the garden. Can you find all five?

Wren

Bullfinch

Goldfinch

Great Tit

Robin

Summer Fair

The unicorns are holding a summer fair in the garden. Look at this scene for two minutes, then turn the page and try to answer all the questions without looking back.

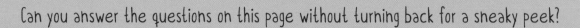

It's time to put your magical memory to the test!

Can you answer the questions on this page without turning back for a sneaky peek?

1. What animal is on the merry-go-round?

· ·

2. What sweet treats are the unicorns selling at their stall?

· ·

3. How many unicorns are playing on the bouncy castle?

· ·

4. What colours are the manes of the unicorns bobbing for apples?

· ·

5. How many sunflowers can you see?

· ·

6. What is the unicorn wearing a flower crown doing?

· ·

There's nothing better than an ice cream
to cool you down on a hot summer's day.

List your favourite ice-cream flavours here:

1. ....

2. ....

3. ....

4. ....

5. ....

6. ....

7. ....

8. ....

9. ....

10. ....

Autumn Garden

As the unicorns enter the Autumn Garden, the wind begins to blow. Leaves are turning orange, red and brown and animals are busily preparing for the cold weather to come.

Colour in this picture using your favourite autumnal colours.

The unicorns are kicking up the crunchy leaves with their hooves.
One unicorn is seeing how many leaves of different shapes she can spot.

Can you match the leaves to their silhouettes?

Leaf Art

Leaves have lots of interesting patterns and textures. Capture their special shapes with this leaf art activity.

You will need:

- dry leaves
- thin white paper
- wax crayons

Ask an adult to help you with this simple gardening activity.

Step one: with a grown-up, go for a walk near your home and collect a selection of leaves. Pick dry leaves in different colours from the ground. Do not pull leaves off branches as you could damage the tree.

Step two: choose one leaf and lay it on a flat surface with the bottom side facing up. Put your piece of paper over the top.

Step three: using the side of your wax crayon, gently rub over the area, until the whole leaf appears.

Step four: now choose another leaf to rub and repeat the above steps. See what patterns you can make by overlapping the leaves and using different colours.

Brilliant Bird Feeder

Help to feed hungry beaks with this D.I.Y. bird feeder.
It can be hung up high in your garden, or even out of a window.

You will need:

- a clean, empty milk carton or plastic drinks bottle
- scissors
- brown paint
- a paint brush
- string
- birdseed

Bird food often contains nuts, so avoid this activity if you have a nut allergy.

Be careful when using scissors. Make sure there is a grown-up around to help with this activity.

64

Step one: cut a round 10 cm hole in the side of your plastic milk bottle or drinks bottle.

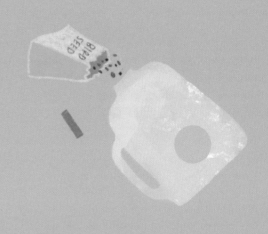

Step two: paint your bird feeder brown paint and leave it to dry.

Step three: pour in some birdseed, so that it fills the bottle right up to the bottom of your hole.

Step four: use a pin to make a hole in the side of the bottle, near to the base. Use scissors to widen the hole slightly, then push a stick through it for the perch. Loop the string round the neck of the bottle.

Step five: ask a grown-up to tie it securely to a tree in your garden or out of a window.

Pumpkin Patch

It's harvest time, so the unicorns have galloped over to the pumpkin patch.
Follow the trail to discover which giant orange pumpkin they're going to pick.

A.   **B.**   **C.**

The unicorns are carving funny faces into their pumpkins.
Doodle your own pumpkin design.

Pumpkins are planted in May or June and harvested in the autumn. They need plenty of water to make sure big, healthy fruits grow.

Trip to the Treetops

High up in the branches, the unicorns have discovered an amazing tree house. Colour in the treetop scene.

How many squirrels can you spot?

Perfect Pencil Pot

Create a pot to store your special pens and pencils in
using bits and bobs gathered from the garden.

You will need:

- clean, empty garden pot
- coloured tissue paper
- safety scissors
- liquid glue
- a selection of small twigs
- elastic band
- ribbon
- biodegradable glitter (optional)

When using scissors, ask a grown-up to help you.

Step one: if your pot is dirty, clean it with warm, soapy water. Once dry, cover your pot with tissue paper and glue it in place.

Step two: wrap two elastic bands around the pot, one at the top and one at the bottom.

Step three: choose twigs that are a little longer than the empty pot or snap bigger twigs down to the right size (be careful to avoid splinters) and slot them beneath the elastic bands.

Step four: work your way around the pot until it is completely covered by twigs. Some of your tissue paper will peep through, so make sure you choose a colour you like.

Step five: tie a length of ribbon over the elastic bands to hide them and then, if you like, add a little glitter to make your pot extra pretty. Now fill it up with your favourite pencils.

Out and About

There are lots of amazing things to look out for in the garden. Can you think of seven things you might spot? Try and find something for every letter of the word MAGICAL.

M — milipede

....

A — acorn

....

G —

....

I —

....

C —

....

A —

....

L —

....

Remember to look out for these things when you're next out exploring in a garden or park!

In autumn, many animals start to get ready
for their winter hibernation.

What favourite things do you enjoy when you're cosy indoors?

Favourite foods to eat:

....

....

Favourite books to read:

....

....

Favourite movies to watch:

....

....

Favourite games to play:

....

....

Winter Garden

The unicorns have entered the Winter Garden. The branches are bare and snow is falling softly all around. Can you spot six differences between the two snowy scenes?

Wonderful Wreath

Create a pretty wreath with some wonderful winter greenery.

You will need:

- a selection of winter greenery, such as mistletoe, fir sprigs and pine sprigs
- metal coat hanger
- floristry wire
- safety scissors
- ribbon or piece of string

Be careful when using scissors. Make sure there is a grown-up around to help with this activity.

76

Step one: ask a grown-up to stretch the metal coat hanger into a circle shape, easing out any kinks.

Step two: lay your coat hanger on a flat surface and arrange your greenery so the hanger is completely covered — the bushier the better!

Step three: ask a grown-up to wrap the floristry wire around the greenery to secure it in place. They might need to wrap it in multiple places, to make sure nothing falls off.

Step four: tie your ribbon or string around the coat hanger hook and hang your wreath up somewhere cool and airy.

Slippery Hooves

The sparkling frozen lake is the perfect place for the unicorns to practise their skating. Add some wintery colours to the chilly picture.

snowy surprises

The unicorns are decorating a festive tree, but they can't find their favourite bauble. It's round, red and has four green stripes. Can you spot and circle it for them?

These talented unicorns have been carving ice with their horns.
Design your own unicorn sculpture in the space below.

Fabulously Frosty Mobile

Hang up these icy decorations in the garden on cold wintery days, then watch them as they spin and sparkle.

You will need:

- plastic or metal tray
- biscuit cutters (stars or hearts will work brilliantly.)
- a selection of interesting leaves, or pressed flowers saved from the summer
- string
- jug
- water

Make sure there is a grown-up around to help with this activity.

Step one: arrange your biscuit cutters in a row across the tray, leaving a gap between each one.

Step two: place a leaf or flower in the middle of each shape.

Step three: lay the string between each shape, making sure it touches the tray in the centre of each cookie cutter, so that it will freeze, too.

Step four: fill a jug with water and carefully pour it into each shape. If it's a very cold day (below four degrees centigrade) you can put your tray outside to freeze, but otherwise, slide it carefully into the freezer.

Step five: leave your mobile for a few hours, or overnight, until it's completely frozen. Ask a grown-up to help you ease out the shapes and then hang your sparkling mobile on a fence or between the branches of a tree.

Snowball Fight

Join the unicorns for some wintery fun and doodle in more detail to the scene.

Draw another ten snowballs for the unicorns' game.

Finish off the
snow-unicorn.

Follow these hoofprints to find out
where one of the unicorns is hiding.

Seasonal Souvenirs

It's almost time for the unicorns to head home, but first they want to collect something special to remind them of their magical day. Which item belongs to which season?

SPRING: ·

SUMMER: ·

AUTUMN: ·

WINTER: ·

Holly leaf

Sunflower

Conker

Daffodil

Nature Collector

It's easy to start your own special collection of souvenirs found in nature. Keep your eyes open when you're out and about.

You will need:

- small cardboard box (a shoebox will work perfectly)
- paints
- paint brushes
- notebook or a piece of paper
- pens or pencils

You will need the help of a grown-up with this activity. You'll need to ask permission before going outside and collecting your nature souvenirs.

Step one: use paints to decorate your box. You could add flowers, leaves, animals, or perhaps give it a unicorn theme.

Step two: spend some time exploring your garden or a local park in search of things to fill your box with. Look out for conkers, acorns, seeds, leaves, flowers feathers, sticks and stones.

Step three: make a note of each object you find in your notebook or on your piece of paper. Write down the month, where you found the object and any other details you want to remember, such as any animals you spotted or what the weather was like.

Step four: try this every month, and slowly you'll build up a special seasonal collection. As the seasons change, you'll notice your garden and the park change, too. Write down any differences you spot.

winter wonderland

When the chilly winter weather hits, it's so nice to get all wrapped up.
Draw a cosy scarf, hat and coat for this unicorn so she doesn't get chilly.

Home Time

The unicorns are having one last trot around the garden.

Guide each unicorn through the maze until they all meet in the middle.

Start

Start

Finish

Start

Start

Make Your Own Unicorn Garden

Create your own enchanting garden for visiting unicorns, complete with a magical pond and special fairy bridge.

You will need:

- large plant pot
- potting compost
- a selection of pebbles
- brightly coloured paints
- paint brushes
- water
- recycled plastic cup or pot
- small bowl (no wider than the height of your recycled plastic cup)
- twigs or recycled ice-lolly sticks
- liquid glue
- a selection of seeds, small plants or flowers
- a selection of interesting objects from around the garden, like acorns and pine cones
- unicorn toy (optional)

Gardening can be tricky, so it's best to ask for help from a grown-up.

Step one: fill your large plant pot with potting compost, leaving a space to put your bowl in (this will be your pond).

Step two: place your bowl into the hole, patting the potting compost around it gently. Fill it with water.

Step three: surround your bowl with pebbles to ensure it stays in place. You could paint your pebbles with rainbow colours first, if you like.

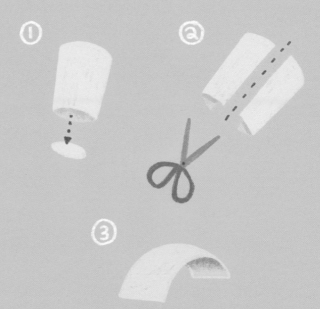

Step four: to make a bridge, cut out the bottom of the plastic cup and then cut it in half vertically. You will just need one half of the cup for this project, so put the other bits aside for future crafting.

Step five: lay your cup over your pond, to check the arch stretches all the way across. Snap the twigs or ice-lolly sticks so they are a little wider than the plastic cup.

Step six: cover your bridge with glue and then lay each of the twigs or ice-lolly sticks side by side, so the cup is completely covered. Leave to dry for a couple of hours, then paint another layer of liquid glue over the top.

Step seven: while your bridge is drying, you can plant your seeds, small plants or flowers as per packet instructions. Try to pick bright, healthy plants that will bring a splash of colour to your garden.

Step eight: get creative with the rest of your unicorn garden — you could make a pebbly path, a miniature rockery or even a wildlife corner.

Step nine: once your bridge is dry, pop it in place over the pond, ready for your unicorns to trot over.

Step ten: add a unicorn toy, if you have one, and watch out for all the minibeasts that will come by and explore.

Gardening Terms

bark The outer layer of a tree's trunk.

bloom To produce a flower.

bulb A round plant bud that begins to grow underground.

cactus (plural is cacti) A plant that has a thick stem, no leaves and often has spines. Cacti grow in hot and dry places.

compost A type of soil, good for growing plants in. Garden compost for adding to soil is made from a mixture of rotting matter, such as leaves, kitchen scraps and grass. Potting compost is good for growing plants in pots in.

coniferous Trees that produce cones — many keep their leaves all year round, such as pine trees and fir trees.

cultivate When you cultivate land or crops, you prepare land and grow crops or plants on it.

deciduous Plants and trees that lose their leaves at certain times of the year, such as oak trees and maple trees.

evergreen Plants and trees that keep their leaves all year round, such as holly and palms.

floret A small flower, often one that makes up part of a bigger flowerhead.

flower The part of a plant that blooms, has petals and makes fruits or seeds.

germinate When a seed begins to sprout.

harvest Collecting seeds or picking fruits, vegetables or other edible plants.

herb A plant which is used to flavour food.

nectar A sugary liquid in flowers that plants use to attract pollinating animals.

orchard An area where fruit trees grow.

pollen Fine grains produced by the male parts of flowers that combine with the female parts of plants to produce seeds.

pollination The process where pollen is moved from a male part to a female part of a plant, or between plants, so the plant can produce seeds.

pollinator Animals that cause pollination to happen by transferring pollen, such as bees, bats and birds. Some plants are pollinated by the wind.

root The part of the plant which gives it support by attaching it to the ground. The roots also carry water and nutrients from the soil to the rest of the plant.

seed A small part of a plant from which new plants grow.

seedling A young plant that has developed from a seed.

sow To plant seeds.

stem The stalk of a plant.

trowel A small garden tool with a pointed scoop.

weed A plant that gardeners want to pull up because it is pushing out its neighbouring plants or growing in the wrong place.

Answers

Pages 12–13

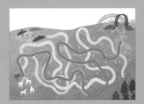

Pages 16–17

Page 26

Pages 28–29

Page 30

1.   2.   3.

Page 32

Page 35

Pages 36–37

Pages 42–43

Sunflowers

Pages 44–45

1–E, 2–A, 3–D, 4–B, 5, C

There are seven slugs.

Pages 52–43

There are 17 green apples and 12 red apples.

The missing fruit is pineapple.

Pages 54–45

Page 58

1. Swans are on the merry-go-round.
2. The unicorns selling are selling cupcakes at their stall?
3. There are two unicorns playing on the bouncy castle.
4. The manes of the unicorns bobbing for apples are pink and purple.
5. There are six sunflowers.
6. The unicorn wearing a flower crown is eating an ice-lolly.

Page 61

Page 66

Path C leads you to the unicorn's giant pumpkin.

Page 68

There are six squirrels.

Pages 74–75

Page 80

Page 89